I Am the Cheese

by
Robert Cormier

Student Packet

Written by
Mary L. Dennis

Contains masters for:

2 Prereading Activities
1 Study Guide
4 Vocabulary Activities
2 Literary Analysis Activities
3 Critical Thinking Activities
3 Writing Activities
2 Crossword Puzzles (Vocabulary, Review)
2 Comprehension Quizzes (two levels)*
2 Unit Exams (two levels)*

PLUS Detailed Answer Key

Level II is more difficult than Level I.

Note

The text used to prepare this guide was the Laurel Leaf softcover published by Bantam Doubleday Dell, ©1977 by Robert Cormier. If other editions are used, page numbers will vary.

Please note: Please assess the appropriateness of this book for the age level and maturity of your students prior to reading and discussing it with your class.

ISBN 1-58130-581-8

To order, contact your local school supply store, or—

Novel Units, Inc.
P.O. Box 791610
San Antonio, TX 78279

Web site: www.educyberstor.com

Name_____

Directions
Rate each of the following statements before you read the novel. Compare your ratings with a partner's, and discuss why you chose the particular ratings you did. After you have completed the novel, rate the statements again.

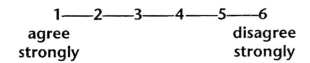

1————2————3————4————5————6
agree   disagree
strongly   strongly

		Before	After
1.	There is no problem without a solution.	____	____
2.	All would be well in this country if everyone tried a little harder to be nice to each other.	____	____
3.	Today's school bully is tomorrow's FBI agent.	____	____
4.	Anyone can be a victim of government corruption.	____	____
5.	It is important to speak out against wrong-doing even at risk to your own life.	____	____
6.	Teens should not read books that don't have hopeful endings.	____	____
7.	Society often destroys its most innocent and most moral members.	____	____
8.	It's hard sometimes to tell who the bad guys are.	____	____
9.	Everyone is expendable.	____	____
10.	Fear is the most powerful motivator of human behavior.	____	____
11.	There is really no such thing as an accident.	____	____
12.	There are two kinds of people in the world: victims and victimizers.	____	____
13.	It is not wise to challenge government institutions.	____	____
14.	"The reward of a thing well done is to have done it." (Emerson)	____	____
15.	"Keep your mind level when life's path is steep." (Horace)	____	____
16.	"Truth never hurts the teller." (Browning)	____	____
17.	It is impossible for evil to exist without the existence of good.	____	____

Name_____

Directions
Below are sentence-starters to be completed before reading each section of the novel as indicated. Answers may be discussed either before or after reading.

Pages 1-38

1. If I was riding my bike in a deserted area and a ferocious-looking dog rushed

   toward me _____.

2. People who go to psychiatrists _____

   _____.

Pages 39-65

3. A happy memory I have from childhood is _____

   _____.

4. Love at first sight _____

   _____.

Pages 66-90

5. Parents keep secrets from children because _____

   _____.

6. The best way to deal with bullies _____

   _____.

Pages 91-115

7. Something I'd like to forget is _____

   _____.

8. When you see someone on the road who needs help _____

   _____.

Pages 116-144

9. If someone in my family was receiving death threats _____
_____.

10. Doing what is right for your country _____
_____.

Pages 145-171

11. If I had to start my life over in a new place _____
_____.

12. My mother worries about _____
_____.

Pages 172-200

13. When you begin to feel suspicious of someone you have trusted _____
_____.

14. When someone is having a panic attack _____
_____.

Pages 201-221

15. People who think the government exists to protect them _____
_____.

16. When one person tries to fight against impossible odds _____
_____.

Directions
Write a brief but concise answer to each question. Starred questions ask for your opinion; there are no "right" or "wrong" answers to these questions.

Pages 1-38

1. Adam says he is a coward (page 12). What things scare him?

*2. Where do you think Adam's father lives?

*3. What kind of pills do you think Adam threw down the garbage disposal?

4. Who is the "T" of the taped interviews? Who is the "A"?

5. What do you notice about the narrative voice on page 17?

*6. Why do you think Cormier included the chapter about the old man in Aswell (pages 22-25)?

7. What was Adam's early childhood like?

*8. Where do you think Adam "goes" when he "steps outside himself" (page 34)?

*9. Do you find anything odd about the incident with the dog?

Pages 39-65

1. Why is Adam "wary...on guard, distrustful" (page 40)?

2. What do you learn about Adam's father's real interests, i.e., when did he "emerge as a person"?

*3. Why do you think Adam and his father ran into the woods?

4. Why does Adam try to call Amy Hertz? How did meeting Amy change Adam?

5. What were Adam's concerns about his mother?

*6. Was Amy's "Number" at the A&P funny to you?

7. What amazed Adam about his response to Amy's phone call about the editor from Rawlings?

6

Pages 66-90

*1. Does Adam's ability to handle—and even enjoy—the rain (page 67) surprise you?

*2. Why do you think Brint is so persistent? Does he seem to be getting more impatient with Adam than he was on previous tapes?

 3. What did Adam find in his father's locked files?

*4. Do you think Adam really enjoyed doing the "Numbers" with Amy?

*5. Do you think Adam is correct when he suggests that Brint already knows everything about him, even Adam's "blank spots"?

 6. Why is Adam so upset after he listens in on his mother's phone call?

 7. Who are Whipper, Dobie, and Lewis?

Pages 91-115

 1. Why does Adam want to see Brint at 2:15 in the morning? What is Brint's reaction?

 2. Why does Adam feel happy on page 96—and why does this feeling quickly vanish?

*3. Who do you think "the gray man" might be?

*4. Is there anything Adam could have done to escape from Whipper and his friends in the car?

*5. Why do you think Adam is silent on Tapes OZK009 and OZK010?

*6. How did you feel when Edna and Arnold came to Adam's rescue?

Pages 116-144

 1. Why was Adam given a number of injections?

 2. How did Adam's father become part of a government investigation?

*3. Do you think Mr. Delmonte/Farmer had any idea what he was getting into when he agreed to testify? Would you want your father to do it?

---

4. What incidents scared Delmonte enough to agree to be part of the Department of Re-Identification's protection program?

*5. What do you think Adam means when he tells Brint, "I sometimes wonder what's more important—what I find out about myself or what you find out about me" (page 131)?

6. What "insurance policy" did Grey provide for the family?

Pages 145-171

1. How does Adam feel when he realizes his bike is missing?

2. In what other part of the book did Adam run down a narrow alley?

3. Why did Grey sometimes probe Adam's father for information?

4. What did Grey's interrogations of Adam's father have in common with Adam's sessions with Brint?

5. What explanation does Adam give for the phone calls to Martha?

*6. Why do you think Brint is uninterested in Adam's mother? Don't most psychiatrists ask a patient about both parents?

7. What secretly-hidden items did Adam's mother show him? Where have you seen some of these items before?

8. How does session OZK013 end?

Pages 172-200

*1. Why do you suppose Adam was worried about being questioned by the police—or being found with something as harmless and legal as aspirin?

*2. To what do you attribute Adam's bravery in confronting Junior Varney about the bike?

*3. Why do you think Adam suddenly misses his mother so much? When he left home, he didn't even let her know he was leaving or tell her goodbye.

4. What reasons does Adam give Brint for doubting him?

5. What was the "Number" at the wedding like?

6. Why was Adam's mother's face "the color of fog" when Adam came home?

7. What was so disconcerting to Adam about the phone call he tried to make to Amy?

*8. What does the gas station attendant tell Adam about the cabins? Why do you think Adam "loses it"?

Pages 201-221

1. What is ironic about Adam's father telling him, "That's what makes [Grey] so good at his job" (page 202) and his mother later saying, "Let's be glad it's them" (page 205)?

2. Who is "Him. Him. Walking toward him and his mother, tall, saw him tall, taller than ever..." (page 208)?

3. What happens after Brint elicits the information from Adam about what happened on the road?

4. What is "Rutterberg" like?

5. What characters do we meet again at the hospital? Who were they in Adam's fantasy trip?

6. Adam asks Dr. Dupont if his father is dead. Is he? How do you know?

7. What was in the package?

8. For how many years has Adam been at the institution? How many times has Brint questioned him? What are Brint's findings? What are his recommendations?

*9. Why was Grey investigated? Do you think Grey is guilty?

10. Why does Adam say, "I am the cheese"?

*11. What do you think will become of Adam? Do you think he knows more than he has told? Is there any hope for him?

Name_____

Directions

In the questions below, vocabulary words are in boldface type. For each one, circle "yes" or "no." In the space below each statement, write a sentence using the word correctly.

1. Would you feel **claustrophobic** out in the open air?   yes   no

2. If a stranger gives you a **menacing** look, should you be cautious?   yes   no

3. Does **momentum** stop you in your tracks?   yes   no

4. If your parents agreed **tentatively** to buy you a car, would that mean they had made a definite decision?   yes   no

5. Would you say that Buddhists and Catholics are **philosophically** different?   yes   no

6. Are **cunning** people clever?   yes   no

7. Are **futile** attempts effective?   yes   no

8. If something is done **irrevocably**, can you change it?   yes   no

9. Could you be **assailed** by guilt?   yes   no

10. If you are **resolute**, are you about to give up?   yes   no

Name_____

Directions
An analogy is a comparison. Samples:
COLD is to HOT as OFF is to ON.
HILL is to MOUNTAIN as STREAM is to RIVER.

I. Use words from the vocabulary list below to complete the analogies.

lucid 71	shroud 93	grimace 86	ravenous 67	admonishment 82
metallic 110	abrupt 69	void 92	torrent 66	reverberates 104

1. FULL is to REPLETE as EMPTY is to _____.

2. DERANGED is to SANE as IRRATIONAL is to _____.

3. TRICKLE is to DRIP as DOWNPOUR is to _____.

4. GRIN is to SMILE as _____ is to SCOWL.

5. REVEAL is to UNCOVER as ENVELOP is to _____.

6. _____ is to REPROVING as COMPLIMENT is to AFFIRMING.

7. HARMONIOUS is to SOFT as _____ is to GRATING.

8. PORTENDS is to WARNS as ECHOES is to _____.

9. SATISFIED is to SATED as _____ is to FAMISHED.

10. GRADUAL is to SUDDEN as EXPECTED is to _____.

II. On a separate sheet of paper, use each of the ten vocabulary words in a sentence.

Name_____

Directions
On the word list, find the answer for each puzzle clue and fill it in.

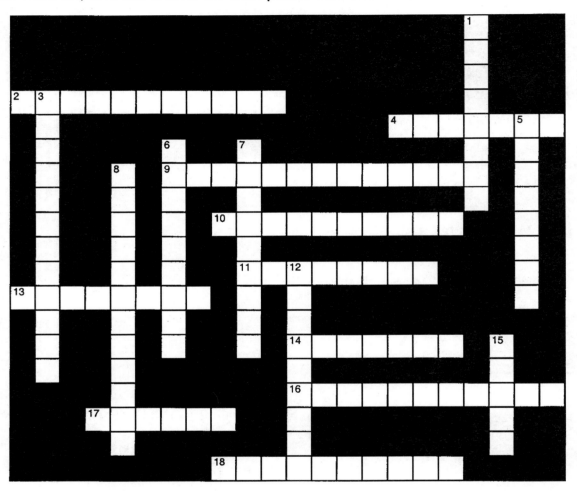

WORD LIST

appalled	indictments
assimilated	intimacy
banal	investigative
compliant	legitimate
desecrate	paranoid
dispensation	phantom
diversion	recoiled
docile	subterfuge
idyllic	surveillance

Across
2. absorbed
4. utopian
9. probing
10. lawful
11. drew back
13. distrustful
14. illusion
16. accusations
17. mild
18. trick

Down
1. horrified
3. tracking
5. closeness
6. amusement
7. defile
8. permission
12. cooperative
15. commonplace

12

Directions

I. Find a word in the vocabulary box to correctly complete each sentence.

anguish 174	belligerently 175	impact 175	reiterate 178
meager 178	turbulent 179	fugitive 180	execution 181
sporadically 181	chasm 181	grappled 183	fester 185
predator 186	crevices 189	buoyant 190	predicament 190
burlesque 195	enunciating 196	languidly 198	metronome 202
reminiscing 204	meandering 205	vista 206	irrefutable 207
lacerated 208	holocaust 211	flourish 212	inducement 218
advisory 219	priority 219	obliterates 220	

1. Junior Varney spoke __ __ __ __ __ __ __ __ __ __ __ __ __ to Adam.

                    1

2. "How many times must I __ __ __ __ __ __ __ __ __ that I am your guide to the past?"

                                       2

3. Cars arrived __ __ __ __ __ __ __ __ __ __ __ in the church parking lot.

                      3   15

4. When Adam's father went along with the game, his voice was __ __ __ __ __ __ __.

                                                                 5

5. The horror of their __ __ __ __ __ __ __ __ __ __ __ became real to Adam.

                        6   10

6. Adam thought about telling Amy he was a __ __ __ __ __ __ __ __ on the run.

                                              13

7. The windshield wipers swung like a __ __ __ __ __ __ __ __ __.

                                11   4

8. The Farmers got out of the car at a scenic __ __ __ __ __.

                                   7

9. Adam found "Rutterberg" deserted, as if there had been a __ __ __ __ __ __ __ __ __.

       9   8

10. __ __ __ __ __ __ __ __ __ of medication had failed to bring forth the information Brint hoped to get from Adam.

     12   14

II. Transfer the letters in the numbered spaces to the spaces below to see a key statement about the novel.

__ __ __ __ __ __ __ __ __ __ __ __ __ __ __

1 2 3 4 5   6 7   8 9 10 11 12 13 14 15

III. Use at least ten of the remaining words in the vocabulary box to make a puzzle like this one, and give it to a partner to solve.

Directions

Brint is constantly asking Adam to look for "clues" to his past. He also points out certain memories as "landmarks." Meanwhile, Adam's bike ride contains some key experiences. As you read, jot down clues and landmarks from Adam's memories (as told to Brint) as well as important events on the bike ride. Look for connections between the two columns, and draw arrows as you find these connections. You may want to jot some notes on the arrows as well.

Clues from Adam's Memories	Events on the Bike Ride

Directions

As you read the novel, you will find out more about the characters on the chart below. You will also see how Adam feels about them, and how they feel about Adam. On the spokes coming from the name circles, write adjectives describing the characters. On the arrows *going to the characters*, write how Adam feels about them. On the arrows *going toward Adam*, write how the characters feel about or treat him.

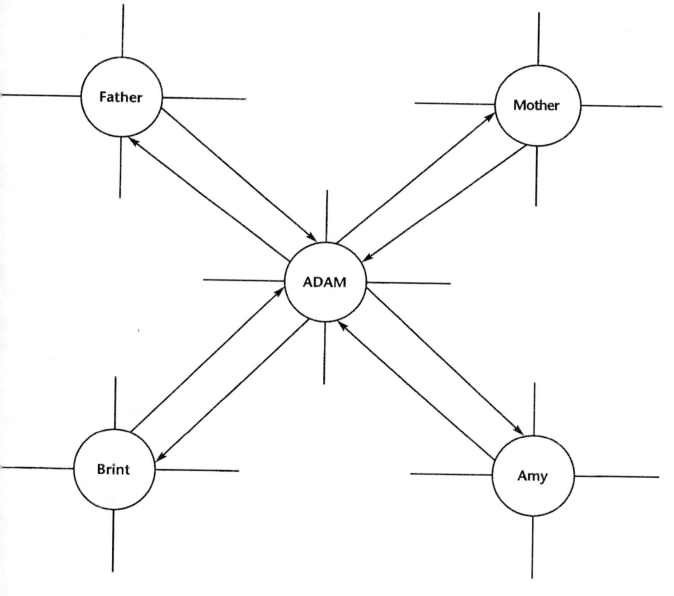

15

Directions
Imagine that you are Adam's father. You have uncovered documents that reveal high-level corruption and possible connections between the government and organized crime. You have been asked to testify in an upcoming trial.

On the chart below, write reasons FOR agreeing to testify under "yes." Write reasons AGAINST testifying under "no." *Remember that you do not know at this point what the final outcome will be*—but you may have some suspicions about what could happen.

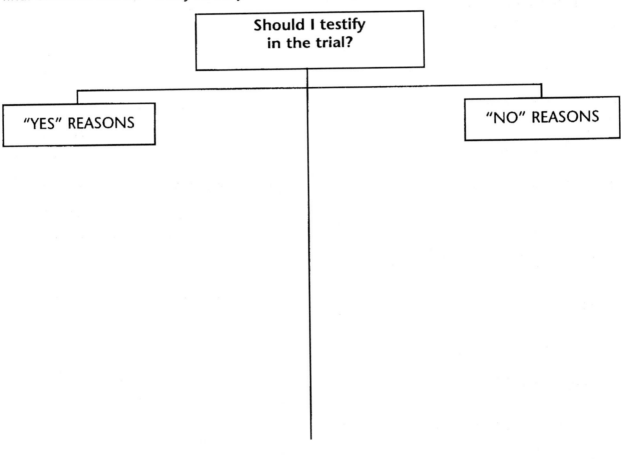

Should I testify in the trial?

"YES" REASONS

"NO" REASONS

Evaluate the reasons you wrote down under "yes" and "no." Do you go ahead and agree to testify—or do you decide against it?

_____

In a well-organized paragraph, state your reasons for your decision.

Name_____

Directions

A **simile** is a type of figurative language where two things are compared. Similes often include the words "like" or "as." For example, Adam says that Mr. Hertz "speaks with emergency in his voice, his sentences like headlines" (page 14).

I. Read each simile, below, and identify what two objects or ideas are being compared. Then explain how these two things are alike.

1. "I pedal through the town, across a wooden bridge, the sound of the slats like applause in my ears" (page 38).

     _____ is like_____ because both_____.

2. "…crashing through brush as if they were on safari in Africa" (page 44).

     _____ is like_____ because both_____.

3. "The car's grille looks like the grinning mouth of some metal monster" (page 103).

     _____ is like_____ because both_____.

4. "His thoughts scurried, like rats in a maze" (page 157).

     _____ are like_____ because both_____.

5. "There's something strange in the stare, as if I am alien…" (page 198).

     _____ is like_____ because both_____.

6. Write and analyze another simile from the story here:

     _____

     _____

     _____

     _____

     _____

II. On the back of this paper, create your own similes by rewriting #1-5, above.

Project: Investigative Report

Directions

You are an investigative reporter for a new television program, "The Real Truth." Your producers have given you an assignment to interview Dr. Dupont, the director of a mental institution in Massachusetts. You've received a tip that some of the hospital's residents are not receiving the help they need—that there are some sinister secrets about this mental hospital. Dr. Dupont has agreed to be interviewed and to let you film some of the residents engaged in their daily activities.

Step One: Watch some investigative television programs like "60 Minutes," "20/20," or "Inside Edition." Notice what kinds of questions the reporter asks, what kinds of responses he or she gets, and what the video portion shows.

Step Two: Make a list of questions you will ask Dr. Dupont. **Examples:** How long has he been the director of this institution? Who hired him? How does he describe its purpose? How many of the residents are expected to be rehabilitated? Are relatives and friends allowed to visit? Who are the other staff members, and how qualified are they to work with the patients? What kinds of drugs do they use here? Who is the young man in the funny hat riding his bike?

Step Three: What will the video portion of your report show? Will you begin by driving through the gates and up the driveway? Will Silver run out barking? Who is sitting on the front porch? What parts of the hospital does Dr. Dupont show you? Are there any areas he refuses to let your cameraman film? Does he let you talk to any residents? What else does your TV audience see? Plan your video portion below.

Scene 1:

Scene 2:

Scene 3:

Scene 4:

Scene 5:

Scene 6:

Scene 7:

Scene 8:

Step Four: On separate paper, write the audio portion of your report, scene-by-scene. Include the questions you ask Dr. Dupont and his responses, any conversations you have with patients or staff members, and any sounds you hear.

Step Five: Write the concluding portion of your report, to be given by you back in the studio. What did you discover, if anything? Do you want to encourage your listeners to take any action—such as writing to their congressmen?

Step Six: Extra Credit: Using a video camera, create an actual ten-to-fifteen minute segment for "The Real Truth," and present it to your class.

Irony

An author is using **irony** when he or she makes a straightforward statement that, considering its context, has a very different meaning. The meaning is often subtly humorous.

The irony in *I Am the Cheese* is best appreciated after reading the entire novel. On closer analysis, the reader "knows" the true situation, so many of Adam's statements while he is on the bike ride are ironic.

For example:
> page 38, "I have a feeling that the dog will pursue me forever." (Adam cannot escape Brint or the government agency he represents.)
> page 11, The allusion to Thomas Wolfe, who wrote *"You Can't Go Home Again,"* is ironic because Adam's family could not return home; now Adam can't.

Write a brief explanation of the irony of each example below.

1. Page 31:   "...they (animals) are not rational."

2. Page 35:   "...no rescuers in sight."

3. Page 24:   "They can forge anything today—passports, licenses, you name it."

4. Page 134: "In other words, I could always tell the truth, even if some fancy truth serums were used..."

5. Page 149: "He's always stealing something, someday they're going to put him away."

6. Page 205: "Let's be glad it's them," his mother said.

Name_____

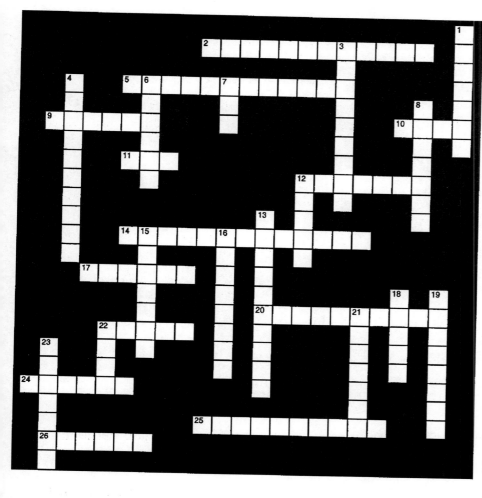

Across

2. Adam wanted to forget this.
5. Adam had these when he became distressed.
9. Kindly doctor at the hospital
10. Switchboard operator
11. The family left for Monument on this.
12. Adam fought to protect his ____.
14. Adam left for Vermont from ____.
17. Junior ____
20. Motel where Adam "lost it"
22. This "doctor" questioned Adam relentlessly.
24. The family's fake name
25. Mr. Farmer was a ____ in Blount.
26. He and Edna helped Adam.

Down

1. He taunted Adam, then chased him down in a car.
3. Mr. Farmer sold this.
4. Drugs given to Adam
6. He stayed on the second floor.
7. She refreshed Adam's spirit.
8. Amy introduced Adam to the ____.
12. This was in the package.
13. Adam's final destination
15. Adam suffered from this mental disorder.
16. The family's religion
18. Adam found two ____ certificates.
19. The family's real name
21. Adam's father was a key one.
22. This was stolen.
23. Mr. Farmer's true ancestry

True-False: Write "T" if the statement is true, "F" if it is false.

_____ 1.   As the story opens, Adam is on a bus on the way to see his father.

_____ 2.   Adam is claustrophobic.

_____ 3.   Adam trusts Brint completely and cooperates with him as much as possible.

_____ 4.   The point of view of this story is first-person present.

_____ 5.   An old man warns Adam that you can't tell the good guys from the bad guys anymore.

_____ 6.   As Adam rides, he keeps singing "Pop Goes the Weasel" to himself.

_____ 7.   As a small child, Adam felt very close to his parents.

_____ 8.   Adam's father's real personality emerged when he talked about books.

_____ 9.   Adam and his father were chased into the woods by a ferocious dog.

_____10.   Amy enjoyed pulling pranks.

_____11.   Adam's mother and Amy's mother were very different.

_____12.   In his father's files, Adam found two passports with different names.

_____13.   Adam was distressed when he listened in on a phone call his mother made.

_____14.   Adam thinks Brint may already know everything about him.

_____15.   Paul Delmonte and "the gray man" are disturbing parts of Adam's past.

_____16.   Whipper, Dobie, and Lewis taunt Adam in a restaurant, but he leaves and doesn't see them again.

Completion: Circle the letter of the word that best completes each statement about *I Am the Cheese.*

17. Adam wondered if it's possible to feel _____ and yet fear open spaces, too.
    A. impaled   B. robust   C. superimposed   D. claustrophobic

18. As Adam headed toward Rutterberg, he felt strong and _____.
    A. raucous   B. nonchalant   C. resolute   D. metallic

19. The rain quickly became a (an) _____.
    A. aura   B. portrayal   C. ravine   D. torrent

20. At times, Adam's memories of the past were clear and _____.
    A. lucid   B. futile   C. tantalizing   D. incessant

21. One thing Adam loved about Amy was that she often spoke _____.
    A. irrevocably   B. tentatively   C. philosophically   D. perilously

22. As Adam stood in the rain, he realized he hadn't eaten and that he was now _____.
    A. subdued   B. exuberant   C. ravenous   D. heady

23. The sound of the car's motor _____ against invisible walls.
    A. distracted   B. reverberated   C. conversed   D. chided

24. When talking to Brint, Adam often felt he had to be clever and _____.
    A. exuberant   B. imminent   C. solicitous   D. cunning

25. The dog looked at Adam and his father and gave a low, _____ growl.
    A. avid   B. menacing   C. hurtling   D. rational

Short Answer: Write a brief answer to each question.

1. As the story opens, where is Adam going, and how does he plan to get there?

2. What is Adam afraid of?

3. How does Adam feel about Brint?

4. What two points of view are used in this novel?

5. As Adam rides, what song does he keep singing, and why?

6. When did Adam's father's real personality emerge?

7. What did Adam and his father meet in the woods?

8. What were Amy's "Numbers"?

9. How did Adam's mother change?

10. What did Adam find in his father's files?

11. Why was Adam distressed when he listened in on a phone call his mother made?

12. Who are Whipper, Dobie, and Lewis?

Completion: Circle the letter of the word that best completes each statement about *I Am the Cheese.*

13. Adam wondered if it's possible to feel _____ and yet fear open spaces, too.
    A. impaled   B. robust   C. superimposed   D. claustrophobic

14. As Adam headed toward Rutterberg, he felt strong and _____.
    A. raucous   B. nonchalant   C. resolute   D. metallic

15. The rain quickly became a (an) _____.
    A. aura   B. portrayal   C. ravine   D. torrent

16. At times, Adam's memories of the past were clear and _____.
    A. lucid   B. futile   C. tantalizing   D. incessant

17. One thing Adam loved about Amy was that she often spoke _____.
    A. irrevocably   B. tentatively   C. philosophically   D. perilously

18. As Adam stood in the rain, he realized he hadn't eaten and that he was now _____.
    A. subdued   B. exuberant   C. ravenous   D. heady

19. The sound of the car's motor _____ against invisible walls.
    A. distracted   B. reverberated   C. conversed   D. chided

20. When talking to Brint, Adam often felt he had to be clever and _____.
    A. exuberant   B. imminent   C. solicitous   D. cunning

Name_____

Identification: Match a character from the box at the right with a description on the left.

___ 1. The old man in Aswell/the maintenance man at the hospital

___ 2. Adam's birth name

___ 3. A cloistered nun, she is Adam's aunt.

___ 4. They gave Adam a ride to Hookset.

___ 5. He and his friends taunted Adam, both in his fantasy and at the hospital.

___ 6. Adam's mother's maiden name.

___ 7. He was also known as #2222.

___ 8. Kindly doctor who brought Adam Pokey the Pig and some of Mr. Farmer's old clothes.

___ 9. This overweight resident of the hospital also appeared in Adam's fantasy on a fire escape.

___ 10. She was Adam's one friend; he tries to call her several times in his fantasy.

A.	Paul Delmonte
B.	Grey
C.	Dr. Dupont
D.	Arthur Haynes
E.	Junior Varney
F.	Anthony Delmonte
G.	Adam Farmer
H.	Louise Nolan
I.	Martha
J.	Luke
K.	Arnold and Edna
L.	Mr. Harvester
M.	Whipper
N.	Brint
O.	Amy Hertz

___ 11. He appears as a counter man in a restaurant, and later as the switchboard operator at the hospital.

___ 12. This ruthless interrogator recommends that Adam be "terminated."

___ 13. In Adam's fantasy, this thief steals his bike, as he often tries to do at the hospital.

___ 14. He is the cheese.

___ 15. The real name of Adam's father, an investigative journalist who testified in a high-level trial.

Multiple Choice: Write the letter of the correct answer on the blank line.

___ 16. Adam takes off on his bike from Monument, Massachusetts. He is planning to visit his father in
   A. Rutland, Vermont   C. Rutterberg, Vermont
   B. Blount, Vermont   D. Belton Falls, New Hampshire

___ 17. The package Adam carries for his father contains
   A. his father's favorite old hat
   B. some files Adam found in the basement
   C. brownies
   D. Pokey the Pig

___ 18. As Adam pedals along, he sings
   A. "Pop Goes the Weasel"
   B. "The Farmer in the Dell"
   C. "I've Got Your Number"
   D. "What Do I Do Without You?"

___ 19. An old man in Aswell advises Adam to watch out, because
   A. people can forge anything these days
   B. you can't tell the good guys from the bad
   C. there is no privacy anymore
   D. all of these

___ 20. Adam's fear of closed spaces, dogs, snakes, and other things can be tied to
   A. early childhood experiences
   B. nothing—they are irrational fears
   C. the panic he feels over his actual present situation
   D. drugs he was given to make him afraid

___ 21. Adam has several close calls with cars during his fantasy bike ride. They can be tied to
   A. the bus accident he was involved in
   B. the time Amy Hertz turned on car radios and windshield wipers
   C. the accident in which Adam's parents were killed
   D. the time Adam's mother tried to drive the car

___ 22. "Animals are not rational" is a good example of Cormier's use of
   A. hyperbole
   B. metaphor
   C. red herrings
   D. irony

___ 23. When Adam tells Brint about the dog he and his father met in the woods, Brint is most interested in
   A. why they went into the woods
   B. what the dog looked like
   C. how Adam felt about the incident
   D. what Adam's father did to fight off the dog

___ 24. When Amy called Adam about the editor from Rawlings, Adam
A. was surprised that his father didn't know the man
B. knew instinctively to lie to Amy
C. asked his mother to tell him about Rawlings
D. told Amy they had never really lived in Pennsylvania

___ 25. Which of the following was not one of Amy's "Numbers"?
A. changing signs on the doors of rooms at the Holiday Inn
B. writing love letters to Mr. Parker
C. filling carts at the grocery store and abandoning them
D. turning on all the windshield wipers and radios in a church parking lot

___ 26. The change in Adam's mother can be attributed to
A. moving away from her home town
B. her innate shyness around new people
C. Mr. Farmer being away from home so much
D. her terror that harm would come to her family

___ 27. Mr. Farmer's love of books can best be explained by the fact that he
A. had an English teacher who inspired him
B. had been a writer before the relocation
C. had worked in a bookstore before the relocation
D. knew Thomas Wolfe personally

___ 28. The fact that Adam, in his fantasy, kept trying to call Amy shows that
A. he doesn't realize he has been at the hospital for three years
B. he thought the man who answered the phone was trying to trick him
C. he is still in love with Amy
D. he had the wrong number

___ 29. When Adam looked in his father's locked files, he found
A. a newspaper article describing an accident
B. proof that his "aunt" was really his mother
C. a document that incriminated the state government
D. two birth certificates, both for him

_____30. Mrs. Farmer's phone call to her sister distressed Adam because
  A. they discussed every triviality of Adam's life
  B. his mother wouldn't let him talk to his cousins
  C. he had been told the family had no relatives
  D. he had not been told about her plans to become a nun

____ 31. Luke came to Adam's rescue when
  A. Whipper and his friends gave Adam a hard time at the restaurant
  B. Adam's bicycle was stolen
  C. Adam was knocked off his bike into a ditch
  D. Silver chased Adam at the hospital

____ 32. What transition best describes Brint as the story unfolds?
  A. kindly psychiatrist to impatient questioner
  B. confident doctor to bewildered doctor
  C. clever investigator to ruthless interrogator
  D. concerned helper to supportive rescuer

____ 33. Adam says, "I'm on the edge of panic half the time" because
  A. he is on the edge of remembering what he'd rather not recall
  B. he is constantly afraid of the injections
  C. Junior, Arthur, and Whipper are always lying in wait for him
  D. he never knows when the dog, Silver, might go after him

____ 34. The "gray man" was
  A. a frequent visitor to the Farmers' home
  B. a liaison between the government program and the Farmers
  C. very probably the Farmers' betrayer
  D. all of these

___ 35. Mr. Farmer's main reason for agreeing to testify in the trial was that
   A. he thought he was acting like a responsible citizen in a free society
   B. he thought his testimony would lead to a promotion in his career
   C. he was trying to protect his family
   D. the government promised to pay for Adam's education

___ 36. Which is not a parallel between Adam's fantasy and his real life?
   A. he takes a trip to Vermont
   B. Junior Varney steals his bike
   C. a frightening dog attacks him
   D. he is rescued by a kindly couple in a station wagon

___ 37. Which of the following is not true?
   A. The Farmers had to trust Grey   C. Amy was part of the conspiracy
   B. Adam had to depend on Brint   D. Both Grey and Brint were ruthless

___ 38. When Adam finally reaches "Rutterberg," the reader realizes
   A. Adam's father is actually Dr. Dupont
   B. Adam and his father are staying at the same hospital
   C. Adam's bike ride was a fantasy
   D. The interviews with Brint were a fantasy

___ 39. Adam pounded on the motel door and begged to be let in because
   A. he was begging to go back to his last happy moments with his parents
   B. he could see there were vacancies but nobody would answer the door
   C. he was symbolically "pounding" on the door to his buried memories
   D. he thought his parents were inside

___ 40. If Adam's father had not testified, what statement about Adam would most likely be true?
   A. He would have ended up in a mental institution anyway, since he was unstable.
   B. He would have grown up in Blount and planned to become a writer.
   C. He and Amy would have gotten married.
   D. He would have become a psychiatrist.

Vocabulary: Match each definition on the right with the correct word at the left.

___ 41.   diversion

___ 42.   idyllic

___ 43.   indictments

___ 44.   paranoid

___ 45.   recoiled

___ 46.   compliant

___ 47.   reiterate

___ 48.   sporadically

___ 49.   vista

___ 50.   holocaust

A.   overly suspicious

B.   utopian

C.   disaster

D.   intermittently

E.   cooperative

F.   drew back

G.   accusations

H.   repeat

I.   view

J.   amusement

Identification: Write the name of the character on the blank next to his or her description.

_____ 1. The old man in Aswell/the maintenance man at the hospital

_____ 2. Adam's birth name

_____ 3. A cloistered nun, she is Adam's aunt.

_____ 4. They gave Adam a ride to Hookset.

_____ 5. He and his friends taunted Adam, both in his fantasy and at the hospital.

_____ 6. Adam's mother's maiden name.

_____ 7. He was also known as #2222.

_____ 8. Kindly doctor who brought Adam Pokey the Pig and some of Mr. Farmer's old clothes.

_____ 9. This overweight resident of the hospital also appeared in Adam's fantasy on a fire escape.

_____ 10. She was Adam's one friend; he tries to call her several times in his fantasy.

_____ 11. He appears as a counter man in a restaurant, and later as the switchboard operator at the hospital.

_____ 12. This ruthless interrogator recommends that Adam be "terminated."

_____ 13. In Adam's fantasy, this thief steals his bike—as he often tries to do at the hospital.

_____ 14. He is the cheese.

_____ 15. The real name of Adam's father, an investigative journalist who testified in a high-level trial.

Short Answer: Write a brief but concise answer to each question.

16. Why does Adam leave Monument, Massachusetts, on his bike?

17. What song does Adam sing as he rides? Why?

18. What warning did an old man in Aswell give Adam?

19. To what do you tie Adam's fear of closed spaces, dogs, snakes, and other things?

20. Adam has several close calls with cars during his fantasy bike ride. To what event in his real life can they be tied?

21. "Animals are not rational" is a good example of Cormier's use of what?

22. When Adam tells Brint about the dog he and his father met in the woods, Brint is most interested in what?

23. When Amy called Adam about the editor from Rawlings, how did Adam's response surprise even him?

24. Describe one of Amy's "Numbers."

25. To what can you attribute the change in Adam's mother?

26. Why did Mr. Farmer love books so much?

27. What did Adam find in his father's locked files?

28. Describe Brint and his treatment of Adam.

29. Who was "the gray man"?

30. What was Mr. Farmer's main reason for agreeing to testify in the trial?

Essay

I. Analysis

Directions: Support or refute one of the following statements. Be sure to cite details and examples from the novel to support your opinion. Be sure to indicate on your paper the letter of the statement you choose.

A. "Through hints, half-truths, the brutal insistence of Brint the questioner and the pathetic delusion of the boy, the author presents his case against the menace of institutional power." (Margery Fisher, *Growing Point,* April 1978)

B. "Adam…is more a victim than a protagonist. If we care about what happens to him, it is not because of any crucial internal decision he must make, but precisely because he is the helpless victim of processes he cannot affect, let alone control." (Anne Scott MacLeod, *Children's Literature in Education,* Vol. 12, No. 2, 1981)

C. "Mr. Cormier is actually writing about integrity; and in the course of doing so, he cogently uncovers the lacerations that evil often inflicts upon the innocent." (Paul Heins, *The Horn Book,* August 1977)

II. Creative/Critical Thinking

Directions: Choose either A, B, or C.

A. Write three entries in Brint's file about Adam after three different sessions: one near the beginning of the novel, one in the middle, and one near the end.

B. Write a poem beginning with the line "The cheese stands alone." Your poem should explain *why* the cheese stands alone.

C. Write a ten-minute script for "Unsolved Mysteries" regarding the mysterious disappearance of the Farmer family.

Answer Key

Note: Answers are not given for open-ended activities, such as Activities #1, #2 and others requiring personal response.

Study Questions

Pages 11-38
1. closed spaces, open spaces, dogs, snakes, animals
2. Personal response
3. Personal response
4. Brint/Adam
5. It changes to third person, past tense.
6. Personal response
7. He felt safe, loved and happy.
8. Personal response
9. Personal response

Pages 39-65
1. He doesn't fully trust Brint.
2. He loved to read and talk about books.
3. Personal response
4. He's in love with Amy; she put him in touch with a less serious side of himself.
5. She had become a reclusive, fearful person.
6. Personal response
7. He knew instinctively that he should lie about his family's past.

Pages 66-90
1. Personal response
2. Personal response
3. two birth certificates for himself, with two different dates
4. Personal response
5. Personal response
6. His mother was talking to his aunt—and he had been told they had no living relatives.
7. three "wise guys" in a restaurant who taunt Adam about his bike and package

Pages 91-115

1. Adam had an anxiety attack; Brint is irritated and suggests medication.
2. He was proud to have stood up to the bullies—but then upset by his call to Amy and by the approach of Whipper, Dobie and Lewis.
3. Personal response
4. Personal response
5. Personal response
6. Personal response

Pages 116-144

1. The injections were supposed to calm him down and help him remember.
2. He uncovered documents regarding corruption on federal and state levels, and a connection with organized crime.
3. Personal response
4. a bomb in his car, an assassin's attempt on his life, threatening calls to his wife
5. Personal response
6. a newspaper article saying the whole family had died in an auto accident

Pages 145-171

1. vulnerable, panic-stricken
2. He and his father ran down an alley into the woods—page 43.
3. Grey was looking for more information, and making sure the mob hadn't "gotten to" Mr. Farmer.
4. Both Grey and Brint probed for information.
5. Special permission was given for his mother to call her sister once a week.
6. Personal response
7. a scarf, a hat, a jacket; Adam is wearing the hat and the jacket on his bike ride.
8. Adam becomes very anxious, wants to know where his parents are.

Pages 172-200

1. Personal response
2. Personal response
3. Personal response
4. He doubts he's a doctor or a psychiatrist; he notices Brint looks only for certain information, is not really interested in him or his feelings.
5. Adam and Amy turned on some radios and windshield wipers in the church parking lot, but were chased away by a janitor.
6. Grey had called suggesting the family leave town for a few days for their own safety.
7. The man who answered said he had had the number for three years.
8. The gas station attendant tells Adam the motel has been closed for two or three years. Personal response

Pages 201-221

1. Grey is probably the one who set them up to be killed.
2. Grey
3. Adam becomes completely unresponsive.
4. It is actually the hospital where Adam is staying.
5. Mr. Harvester=paranoid old man in Aswell; Whipper, Dobie, Lewis=wise guys in lunchroom; Luke=counterman at the lunchroom, always on the phone; Arthur Haynes=lewd fat man on fire escape; Junior Varney=boy who stole Adam's bike in Hookset
6. Yes. Brint's final tape says Adam's father's death was confirmed by Grey.
7. Pokey the Pig
8. three years/three times; Brint doesn't think Adam is hiding anything, and recommends he be "terminated."
9. He was suspected of telling the mob where the Farmers were. Personal response
10. He is completely alone, is in a trap, can only wait for the rats.
11. Personal response

Activity #3: I. 1-no; 2-yes; 3-no; 4-no; 5-yes; 6-yes; 7-no; 8-no; 9-yes; 10-no; Sentences will vary.

Activity #4: I. 1-void; 2-lucid; 3-torrent; 4-grimace; 5-shroud; 6-Admonishment; 7-metallic; 8-reverberates; 9-ravenous; 10-abrupt II. Sentences will vary.

Activity #5: See page 40.

Activity #6: I. 1-belligerently; 2-reiterate; 3-sporadically; 4-buoyant; 5-predicament; 6-fugitive; 7-metronome; 8-vista; 9-holocaust; 10-inducement II. Brint is the enemy. III. Sentences will vary.

Activity #7: Most connections will be made as students reach the end of the novel.

Activity #8: Individual responses will vary, but students might note that Adam's father is a good citizen, loves books, is honest, has a sense of humor, and is protective and caring toward Adam. Adam's mother is fearful, shy, sad, and wishes she could defy Grey. She is worried and solicitous where Adam is concerned. Amy is fun-loving, robust, mischievous, and outgoing, and wants Adam to "lighten up." Brint is ruthless, clever, a good actor, "a robot." He doesn't really care about Adam, just wants information. Adam is amnesiac, confused, scared, alone. He admires and loves his father and feels close to him. He is concerned about his mother and the changes he's seen in her. He fell in love with Amy at first sight. He doesn't really trust Brint.

Activity #9: Personal response.

Activity #10: I. 1-The slats sound like applause because both make a clapping sound, and Adam is proud of himself at this point. 2-Crashing through brush is like being on safari in Africa because both are rough terrain—and in this case, an animal appears. 3-The car's grille is like a monster's mouth because both are frightening and both pursue Adam. 4-His thoughts are like rats in a maze because both move quickly, looking for a way to go. 5-Adam is like an alien because both are like strangers in a land of "normal" people. **II.** Students' similes will vary.

Activity #11: Projects will vary.

Activity #12: 1-Adam himself is less rational than an animal at this point. 2-As in Adam's current situation, there are "no rescuers." 3-The government created phony documents for Adam's family. 4-The "fancy truth serums" <u>are</u> being used. 5-In reality, Junior Varney has been put away. 6-What Adam's mother doesn't know is that Grey has set them up.

Activity #13: See page 40.

Comprehension Quiz, Level I: 1-F; 2-T; 3-F; 4-F; 5-T; 6-F; 7-T; 8-T; 9-F; 10-T; 11-T; 12-F; 13-T; 14-T; 15-T; 16-F; 17-D; 18-C; 19-D; 20-A; 21-C; 22-C; 23-B; 24-D; 25-B

Comprehension Quiz, Level II: 1-He is headed for Rutterberg, Vermont on his bike to see his father. 2- Adam fears open spaces, closed spaces, animals, snakes, dogs. 3-Adam doesn't completely trust Brint. 4-The points of view used in the novel are first-person present and third-person past. 5-He sings "The Farmer in the Dell" because it reminds him of happy times with his parents. 6-Adam's father's real personality emerged when he read or talked about books. 7-Adam and his father met a ferocious dog in the woods. 8-Amy's "Numbers" were pranks she pulled. 9. She changed from a carefree, laughing person to a subdued, fearful one. 10-Adam found two birth certificates with two different dates. 11-Adam's mother was talking to her sister, and Adam had been told they had no living relatives. 12-All three are wise guys in a restaurant who taunt Adam. 13-D; 14-C; 15-D; 16-A; 17-C; 18-C; 19-B; 20-D

Unit Test, Level I: 1-L; 2-A; 3-I; 4-K; 5-M; 6-H; 7-B; 8-C; 9-D; 10-O; 11-J; 12-N; 13-E; 14-G; 15-F; 16-C; 17-D; 18-B; 19-D; 20-C; 21-C; 22-D; 23-A; 24-B; 25-B; 26-D; 27-B; 28-A; 29-D; 30-C; 31-A; 32-C; 33-A; 34-D; 35-A; 36-D; 37-C; 38-C; 39-A; 40-B; 41-J; 42-B; 43-G; 44-A; 45-F; 46-E; 47-H; 48-D; 49-I; 50-C

Unit Test, Level II:

1. Mr. Harvester
2. Paul Delmonte
3. Martha
4. Edna & Arnold
5. Whipper
6. Louise Nolan
7. Grey
8. Dr. Dupont
9. Arthur Haynes
10. Amy Hertz
11. Luke
12. Brint
13. Junior Varney
14. Adam
15. Anthony Delmonte

16. He is going to Rutterberg, Vermont to see his father.
17. "The Farmer in the Dell"; It reminds him of his father.
18. He tells him to watch out for the bad guys—who can no longer be told from the good guys. He tells Adam there is no privacy, and that anyone can forge anything.
19. Adam's identified fears are probably stand-ins for his real fear, the panic he feels at his situation.
20. They can be tied to the accident in which he lost his parents.
21. "Animals are not rational" is a good example of Cormier's use of irony.
22. Brint seems to be most interested in why Adam and his father ran into the woods, not how Adam felt about the incident.
23. Adam was surprised that he instinctively knew he should lie about his family's past.
24. Student answers will vary: the A & P cart-loading, changing door signs at the Holiday Inn, or the prank in the church parking lot.
25. Adam's mother was living in terror that harm would come to the family.
26. He had once been a journalist, loved to read and write.
27. Adam found two birth certificates with his name on them, with two different dates.
28. Brint tried to carry off a ruse of being concerned about Adam, but in reality he was a ruthless interrogator pumping Adam for information. He cared nothing about Adam.
29. Grey was a liaison between the Farmers and the protection program, but in the end he probably set them up to be killed.
30. Mr. Farmer felt it was his duty as a citizen to testify in the trial.

Essay (This may be assigned as a take-home portion.)

I. Analysis

Students who choose **A** should point out several examples of Brint's tenacity in his questioning of Adam and several examples of Adam's innocence and inability to face reality. Finally, they should summarize Cormier's theme of the abuse of the power held by government and, in fact, any large organizations which victimize individuals.

Students who choose **B** might point out that Cormier uses Adam to make his point about the victimization of the innocent by large organizations and institutions. Who Adam really is remains somewhat of a mystery to us, but his function as a victim is clear. Adam as an individual is in conflict with the system, but there is nothing he can do to resolve the conflict.

Students who choose **C** might defend this statement by pointing out that both Mr. Farmer and Adam act honestly. They know nothing about subterfuge. They can't even begin to imagine the reality of their predicaments.

II. Creative/Critical Thinking: Personal response.

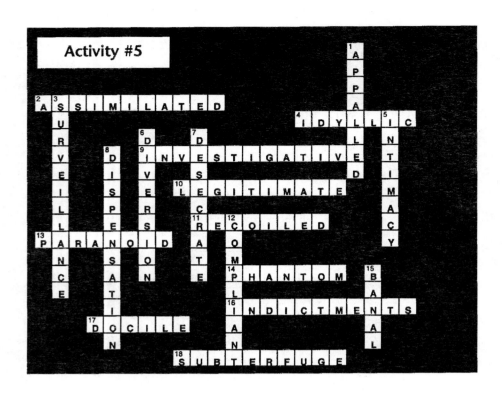

Activity #5

Crossword puzzle answers:
- 2 Across: ASSIMILATED
- 4 Across: IDYLLIC
- 9 Across: INVESTIGATIVE
- 10 Across: LEGITIMATE
- 11 Across: RECOILED
- 13 Across: PARANOID
- 14 Across: PHANTOM
- 16 Across: INDICTMENTS
- 17 Across: DOCILE
- 18 Across: SUBTERFUGE
- 1 Down: APPA(LLED)
- 3 Down: SURVEILLANCE
- 5 Down: INTIMACY
- 6 Down: DIVERS
- 7 Down: DISCO
- 8 Down: DISPESATI
- 12 Down: QOM
- 15 Down: BAAL

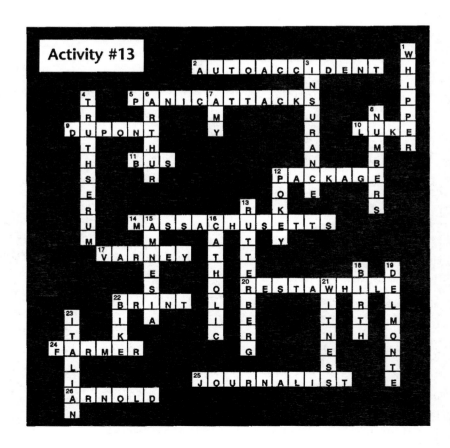

Activity #13

Crossword puzzle answers:
- 2 Across: AUTOACCIDENT
- 5 Across: PANICATTACKS
- 9 Across: DUPONT
- 10 Across: LUKE
- 11 Across: BUS
- 12 Across: PACKAGE
- 14 Across: MASSACHUSETTS
- 17 Across: VARNEY
- 20 Across: RESTAWHILE
- 22 Across: BRINT
- 24 Across: FARMER
- 25 Across: JOURNALIST
- 26 Across: ARNOLD
- 1 Down: WHIPPER
- 3 Down: NAS
- 4 Down: TRHSERUM
- 6 Down: RMY
- 7 Down: MY
- 8 Down: NUMBERS
- 13 Down: RKY
- 15 Down: MMES
- 16 Down: CATHOLIC
- 18 Down: BITHIN
- 19 Down: DELMONTE
- 21 Down: ARTHR
- 23 Down: ITIL